# Slip Slide
# Baseball Jokes

by Gail Tuchman
Illustrated by Tony Griego

SCHOLASTIC

Why did Slim Ump stand on

a stump to see the ball game?

The stump made a grand stand.

Which bug writes

the team names?

The Spelling Bee.

Why can't the Spelling Bee play?

It has hives.

3

What does the team scream

when Bat steps up to the plate?

Bat at bat!

4

What made Bat stick

so close to the plate?

Gum.

Why does the team stand up

when Pop Snake slip slides to bat?

**He hits pop-ups.**

What did Duck do

when the ball sped by?

He ducked.

Why don't ducks tell jokes

when they slide into the plate?

They don't want to quack up.

8

Why did Big Pig steal the base?

**She was a hog.**

Which step does
Fast Fox do when
he steals the base?

**The fox trot.**

Where does Spot go
when he digs?

To the dug out.

What do you call
Spot when he
stands in the sun?

A hot dog.

What did Spot yell to Flea as

he was about to slam the ball?

Don't bug me!

What did Bull use to keep score?

A bull pen.

Why did Speeding Ant stop

to sit down on a stone?

**She was panting.**

Why did Pop Snake spin

and spin and spin?

To put a spin on the ball.

What did Slim Ump call from the

stump at the end of the game?

Pig out!

# My Words

*which

| sl- | sp- | -st- | |
|-----|-----|------|---|
| slam | sped | stand | stone |
| slide | speeding | steal | stop |
| slim | spelling | step | stump |
| slip | spin | stick | fast |
| | spot | | |

**Story Words:** Bull, score, writes

**\*new high frequency words**